THE TIGER
AND THE
JACKAL

Retold by Gill and Paul Hamlyn

Illustrated by Michael Terry

Heinemann

In a land far away there lived a tiger.
One day the tiger was walking in
the jungle when suddenly a trap fell
down on top of him.

He shouted and
called as loudly
as he could but
no one heard him.

Just then an old man came by.

'Please help me,' shouted the tiger.

'Come over here and let me out.'

'I can't do that,' said the old man.

'You will eat me up.'

'I won't eat you up,' said the tiger.
'If you let me out I will be your friend
  for ever.'
'Can I trust you?' asked the old man.
'Yes,' said the tiger. 'You can trust me.'
So the old man walked over to
  the tiger and he opened the trap.

Out jumped the tiger.
He laughed at the old man and said
to him, 'You should never trust a
tiger. Now I'm going to eat you up.'

'Don't eat me yet,'
said the old man.
'Let me ask the
donkey if he thinks
that is fair.'

But when the old man asked the
donkey, the donkey said, 'Why should
I help you? People make me work
hard all day. That is not fair. The
tiger can eat you.'

The old man said to the tiger,
'Don't eat me yet. Let me ask the ox
if he thinks that is fair.'
But when the old man asked the ox,
the ox said, 'Why should I help you?
People make me work hard all day.
That is not fair. The tiger can
eat you.'

The old man tried once more.

'Let me ask the elephant if she thinks that is fair,' he said.

But the elephant said, 'Why should I help you? People make me work hard all day. That is not fair. The tiger can eat you.'

The tiger laughed at the old man.
'See,' he said. 'They all say that
I can eat you up.'

But just then a jackal came by.
He looked at the old man and
the tiger.
'What's going on here?' he asked.

The old man told the jackal how he
had let the tiger out of the trap and
that now the tiger wanted to eat him.
The jackal looked at the tiger and
then he said, 'I don't get it. Tell me
again what happened.'

So the old man told the jackal again
what had happened.
'It's no good,' said the jackal, 'I still
don't get it. You must show me what
happened. Let's go back to the trap.'

The tiger was getting cross but he went with the old man and the jackal back to the trap.

'Now I get it,' said the jackal to the
old man. 'You were in the trap and
the tiger came walking by.'
'No,' shouted the tiger. 'I was the
one in the trap.'

'Now I get it,' said the jackal to the tiger. 'I was in the trap and the old man came walking by.'

'No, no, no,' shouted the tiger.

'I was the one in the trap.'

By now the tiger was very cross.
'I will show you what happened,'
he said to the jackal, and he jumped
into the trap.
'Now do you get it?' he shouted to the
jackal. '**I** was the one in the trap.'

'Yes,' said the jackal. 'Just as you
are now!' and he laughed as he shut
the trap.
Then he said to the old man,
'Don't forget. Never trust a tiger.'